The Friendship Diary

Poems
by

Paige Cunningham

The Friendship Diary

© 2020 by Paige Cunningham
Cover Photo © 2020 by Paige Cunningham
Artist Photo by Mark Garland

Book design by SeaGrove Press

ISBN: 978-0-9993218-9-8
Library of Congress Control Number: 2020944603

Printed in the United States of America

SeaGrove Press
638 Sunset Blvd
Cape May, New Jersey 08204
seagrovepress@gmail.com

DEDICATION

To my husband, Mark Garland, for photos I needed, especially last minute, as I'm yelling, "quick get your camera!"

Thank you to Cindy and Bill Huf whose oasis inspired this project. Without it, none of these poems would have been born.

And to all my friends, I thank you for being a part of my life.

ACKNOWLEDGMENTS

Photo credits ;
Paige Cunningham
Mark Garland
Julie Zickefoose – skunk photo
Kathy Horn – otter photo
Michael O'Brian – opossum photo
Ron Rollet – wind photo

Introduction

Ever since I can remember, I was an outdoors kind of girl. No dolls (although I had loads of stuffed animals). No frills. And no pink. Some people called me a "Tomboy." I didn't mind. I just kept being me, "Tomgirl" Paige, making friends with every bug and animal in our yard and forest and down the street in our neighbor's yards and forests and ponds. I'd even walk the 3 miles to the local Audubon Center to walk their trails. I'd stay out 'til I was blue in winter and wrinkled up (from swimming all day) in summer.

So, it didn't surprise me when I took a job at a nature center exploring the outdoors with kids and adults. Or when I started writing these Friendship Diaries while swimming or walking or sitting outside.

These poems began with Herbert. The day we met was like none other. Neither would be the days that followed that year. Meeting, or should I say seeing, or being in the present moment, with the friends in my backyard and enjoying the quiet, and sometimes not so quiet, moments with them.

Friends come in all shapes and sizes: small, large, short, tall, furry, scaly, feathered, slimy and in all colors of the rainbow. Friends can: play, listen, sit, climb, swim, talk, and even cry with you. Friends fill your heart with love, joy and laughter, but sometimes, anger and sadness. Friendships can be complicated but also simple.

Whether friends are on the ground, in the water, on a tree or in the air, they are our community. Each one, a square in the quilt, sharing their gifts, creating a whole.

I hope you meet new friends, get to spend time with longtime ones and enjoy my friends in this book. Every one has a story.

This book is dedicated to all my friends.

I Am Who I Am - Me At 8

Birds in the treetops
And mud on my feet.
Bugs cover my arms
And my hair isn't neat!

I jump in puddles
And crawl over logs.
I pet slimy slugs
And catch big green frogs.

I dig in the dirt
And count all the bees.
I lie in the grass
And measure the trees.

I build tall tree forts
And small log cabins.
I write fairy tales
Only I can imagine.

I rescue lost kittens
And feed the hummers.
I raise praying mantids
And laugh all summer.

I make goopity goop
And oatmeal cookies.
I play with dust bunnies
And my stuffed Bear, Suki.

I sing to the bats
And talk to fireflies.
I dance with the moon
And wish on starful skies.

I am who I am
And this is a fact.
To be who you are
And celebrate that!

AUTUMN

Autumn Friendship Diary #1

I love surprise visits.
How do friends know when you need one.
Early morning
Blue skies
Waves rolling and crashing
And Louie!
Wait, what…
In broad daylight!
Are you crazy!
You'll be a tasty treat for a gull.
Over hill and dale
Crawling cautiously
On tip toes…
Squawk!!!
Watch out, I yell.
Skitter, scatter, scurry…
Left, right, backwards
Gone…
Down the hole.
Minutes go by
Tick tock , tick tock…
One claw, some legs, an eye
Peeking…
PLOP!
Louie's throwing sand
Digging out
Digging in
Making space.
Winterizing
Home improvements.
Along with six cousins,
I must be sitting on prime real estate!

Autumn Friendship Diary #2

I heard a ruckus
A loud chittering
A begging call?
Who? What? Where?
I went to the back yard,
The noise dimmed.
Walked to the front,
It grew louder.
I peered out the door
This way, that way
Down, over, under…
And then, finally up.
There you were
Flapping wings, fluffing feathers
And screaming your heads off.
Feed me!
Feed me!
Feed me…
NOW!
Landing on the Echinacea flowers
Gwen plucked out a few seeds.
She flew up
Fed the beggars
And flew down.
Up and down
Up and down
Over and over and OVER…
Feeding children is a chore!

Autumn Friendship Diary #3

You came one by one
Then in small groups
Then in waves.
Floating in a sea of blue sky
Your orange and black wings
Like stained glass.
I don't know all your names
But your spirits entrance
Lift our hearts
And bring tears.
We remember our lost loved ones.
Thank you for visiting,
Mom, gram, aunt and friends.
Safe travels to Mexico.

Autumn Friendship Diary #4

Some friends make your heart melt
And you feel all warm and gooey.
Others give you a heart attack
And you jump out of your skin!
Today was the latter.
Swimming in a sun glistening sea
Calm as a cucumber
Peacefully all alone…
SPLASH!
WHAP!
PLUNK!
Startled out of my salty trance
I drink in sea water
Feel something slimy on my leg
And almost sink.
You sure got my attention, Snyder!
"Big fish" stories are likely!

* no photos today

Autumn Friendship Diary #5

Certain friends are hard to read.
Some see you
And head in the other direction.
Some blame you
For a cold winter to come.
Others think
You'll bring a warm winter.
I look and see
Rust and black furry stripes
Scooting along…
Curling up under an orange fallen leaf.
I gently pick you up.
You unfurl and crawl
Along my arm like a gymnast
On a balance beam.
No worries about what's to come
Just enjoying you now
As you are, Sam.

Autumn Friendship Diary #6

The pastel orange, pink glow
Reflecting on the water.
Grayish clouds spread out
Like wisps of wool roving.
The sun dips
The light show begins…
Dark orange, red and crimson
Nature painting the sky.
A rustle in the dune grass
A quick flash of fur
Body hidden
Ears like flags
Twitching and moving,
Silence.
Then you hop across the dune.
Be careful Harriet,
Louie may pinch your paw!

Autumn Friendship Diary #7

Time for planting spring bulbs.
I'm not sure we need more,
We have around 3,000.
Bulb addiction is a thing.
Or is it,
A colorful flower addiction?
I was digging
Hoeing
Planting along peacefully
When…
I discovered you,
Doing your job
Eating detritus
Making dirt
Pooping dirt
Keeping our yard healthy.
When my tool…
Cut off your tail!
You wiggled along…
I was stunned.
I said a prayer.
Thank you Willy,
And please forgive me.

Autumn Friendship Diary #8

Walking along the road
A fine mist falls from the gray sky.
I admire the changing colors
The leaves slowly turning
Preparing for winter.
Gold, pumpkin, crimson, chartreuse…
I stop at the mitten leaves
Looking for a curled one,
A shelter
A tent
A cozy blanket
For this friend, Ken.
Is he in here…
Nope, a spider.
Maybe in this one…
Nope, an asassin bug.
Maybe this one…
Is the perfect leaf.
YES!
There you are
Hiding.
Your big "eyes"
Scaring would be predators.
Patiently waiting for nightfall
To venture out for a meal.
The world is a magical crayon box
Full of colorful joys.

Autumn Friendship Diary #9

Floating in the water
Feeling the sun on my face
Rolling waves holding me up
I'm in my place.
I hear you before I see you.
This happens a lot with friends.
You get to know their laugh or footsteps…
And you know it's them,
Before your eyes do.
I open mine just in time
To see the quintet of pelicans,

Flapping
Gliding
Flapping
To the rhythm of the waves.
Hoping you'll meet me at the jetty
But you continue on
Around the corner.
Sometimes friends pass by
With a quick hello.

Autumn Friendship Diary #10

Today was the day
Our town became
A snow globe of friends.
Every one you know is here, there,
Literally everywhere!
On the beach
In the dunes
In the gardens
Over the promenade
On the deck
In backyards
Along the harbor…
Filling the skies with swirling, diving, floating
Flying patterns and colors.
Incredible!
Amazing!
Magical!
Love all around.

Autumn Friendship Diary #11

Sometimes
While visiting with one friend,
Another shows up.
I heard a whirr
Saw a shadow
And then…
My leg became a landing pad.
Your green chunky body hanging on my jeans.
Your iridescent compound eyes looking up at me.
Was this your first flight?
After…
Crawling out from underground
Shedding your exoskeleton coat
Reborn with cellophane wings.
Welcome to the sunlit world, Clyde.
I lift my leg to get a better view
And your wings give you flight, again.
Sorry I didn't get to spend more time with you
But I look forward to hearing your wing song.

Autumn Friendship Diary #12

Even loud friends
Have quiet moments.
I went in and out
Watering the last of the fall flowers.
The gate door swinging
Back and forth
Back and forth
Back and forth.
I'm not sure why I bent down
But there you were,
Camouflaged in the lichens
Your suction cup toes
Holding onto the gate picket.
No voice
No movement
Just you,
Right in front of me,
Surprise!
Good afternoon, Tilly!

Autumn Friendship Diary #13

It's like being on the morning commuter train,
All packed together
All moving at once
Too many to name.
Flying across the sky
Down the dunes
Over the lighthouse
Into the bushes
Thousands gorging on berries.
Whoosh…
Over the pond
Picking insects off the water.
Whoosh…
Swirling this way and that way
Creating kinesthetic patterns.
Whoosh…
Streaming over the parking lot
A river of aliveness.
Oohs and aahs
Smiles and tears
Amazement and wonder.
Thank you tree swallows,
For the pure magic you perform in our hearts.
But how oh how,
Do you not collide in your flurry of movement!

Autumn Friendship Diary #14

Sometimes I forget
But I know you're there.
I don't always feel you
But I'm surrounded by you.
You're a whisper in my hair
A light touch on my cheek.
I'm breathing you in
My lungs are thankful.

Other times, you're a roar.
A growling force
A lion taking down prey.
Swirling clouds, uprooting trees, picking up houses
Flooding towns, changing lives.

And many days, you're a breeze.
Gently pushing boats
Cooling off a hot day
Making children giggle
As you fly their kites
Or blow their bubbles.
Birds riding your thermals
Leaves twirling and seeds spinning
Water rippling and grasses waving.

Which nickname will you be today?
Windy, breezy, blowy, gusty, blustery, drafty, turbulent
Squally, tempestuous, raging, stormy, airy or fresh.

We need you and love you
But there are days we don't like your choice of actions.
Friends can be a complicated relationship.

Autumn Friendship Diary #15

The fall migration train.
One main terminal
For connecting, switching, stopping.
Our yard seemed to be it.
Hundreds flew in
Flitting from tree to bush to flower stalk,
Splashing in the pond
Drinking from the birdbath.
Seeds of every size, shape and type
Creating a bountiful fall buffet
Advertising itself in the morning light.
Eat here. Eat here. Eat here!
And they did…
Every tree and plant alive,
Bird movement
Bird chattiness
Bird colors
Busy. Busy. Birds!
Hundreds flew out
Connecting to another yard.
Refueling. Resting. Replenishing.
Southbound tonight
Every Tom, Dick and Harry.

Autumn Friendship Diary #16

The radar lights up,
Blue and green dots pulsing.
Our hearts skip a beat.
We know what's happening.
We anticipate the gifts in the morning.
We dream about you.
Awake,
We grab coffee, binocs, and run outside
In the dawn's light.
I look up,
Peer around my yard.
Are you here?
Slowly my eyes adjust.
Then…
The quick flashes of movement
The call notes
The settling in.
Hanging upside down
You show off your golden crown.
You grab bugs from the pine needles.
You flit up and down eating voraciously
After traveling all night.
Then I see a ruby crown
A yellow rump
Too many friends to name
Busy doing their thing, while I do mine.
This morning…
The Christmas feeling wrapped up as birds.

Autumn Friendship Diary #17

The crayon box is open.
The colorful joy
Will make your eyes smile.
Drive the parkway
Take a walk
And witness
The Infinite beauty
That surrounds us.
May your heart be open
To its gift.

Autumn Friendship Diary #18

Every fall
The first one
Steals my heart.
The soft feathers
The bill clacking
Those big eyes.
I look into them
I see your soul.
I wish you a good journey.
Off you go…
Into the star filled night.
Fly high Fern.
Thank you
For being a part of my story.

Autumn Friendship Diary #19

Coat and hat on
Sitting on the deck
Under the royal blue, ebony night.
Purple and white haze
Like spilt milk
Spreads across the sky
Speckled with stars.
I hope
I wonder
I wait.
Longing for the call,
I wait a bit more…
Silence
Peace
Quiet
Nothing tonight.
I retreat inside
Windows open
I ready for bed.
Then, I hear it…
The distinct continuous chorus,
Hard to describe…
Hoarse honking, shrill cries, high pitched quacks.
I run outside
Barefoot, toothbrush in hand.
I stand silent
And listen…
Minutes go by
The sound fades across the Bay…
I dream of snow geese,
Winter is on its way.

Autumn Friendship Diary # 20

You give life
You bring joy
From millions of miles away.
Some days we're too busy to notice,
Your shining light.
The warmth on our face
The shadows created.
We take you for granted
'Til you're not here,
Then we want you.
Other days,
We wish for clouds to hide you.
The sweat pouring off us
The leaves withering
The lakes, a dry bed of cracks.
'Til we're cold
'Til it's dark so early
Then we want you again.
The awkward cycle,
Of wanting a friendship
On our own terms.

Autumn Friendship Diary # 21

You know those friends
Who always nurture,
That's you.
From spring's birth
'Til early autumn,
When you quietly shut down
Revealing your true colors.
You hang on, rustling in the breeze
'Til you don't.
'Til that gust of wind blows
And you take flight
Across the sky…
Swirling
Dancing
Soaring
For the first time,
Free.
'Til you land
Gently touching the ground
Becoming…
A blanket for a woolly bear
Food for the earthworms
A place for a cocoon
And for fun…
I shuffle through you
Crunch, crackle, crunch.
I throw you in the air
Spin, whirl, float…
I make a leaf angel
Swish, swash, swish…
Season after season,
Year after year,
I long to see your face.

Autumn Friendship Diary #22

The smell.
The woodsy fallen leaf smell.
The pine needle,
Musty muddy forest smell.
My nose tingles
My lips smile
My heart feels cozy
Walking in the woods.
The bare branches
An abstract sculpture.
The gray trunks,
Tall pillars reaching for the sky.
The colors crunching under foot
Wafting up "that" smell.
When you appear
Out from the underbrush,
Waddle, waddle, waddle…
Not a care in the world
To join your seven friends
Across the road.
Be careful Tom,
Thanksgiving is coming!
I think I'll have spaghetti.

WINTER

Winter Friendship Diary #1

Dark nights
Warmed by friends
Keeps joy
In our hearts.
Happy Winter Solstice!

Winter Friendship Diary #2

I've known you for decades
Three, I think
Is that possible?
I've watched you grow
Stretch your branches
And reach for the sky.
You've been with me
Standing tall
Through three moves
Sad times
And happy times.
You don't judge.
You listen.
You're just there.
My leaning tree.
And every year you brighten
The whole neighborhood
And my heart
With your lights.
Thank you Charlie
For your unwavering support.

Winter Friendship Diary #3

Dedicated
To all the trees
Who were cut down
And left behind
At the tree stands.
I see you.
You're beautiful.
Thank you.

Winter Friendship Diary #4

Some friends zip into your life…
…and then zip right out.
Touching your soul for a mere nanosecond.
Who knows why they come
And why they leave.
This morning it happened.
One, two, three…
Ninety seven, Ninety eight, ninety nine…
It was a robin river flowing
Over my head
Over our yard
Over the neighborhood.
The river slowed.
They decorated deciduous trees like ornaments.
They flew out of one tree
And into another
Devouring cedar berries as they went.
Their "red breasts" shining in the sun.
Their calls loud,
Like they were chatting at a concert
Yelling over the music.
Back and forth.
Hither and yon.
For miles…
This flying river flowed.
My day began with a heart smile.

Winter Friendship Diary #5

I wait all year
For the first snow.
For peace to fill the air.
It surrounds and covers
All in its wake
Like a down comforter.
Warming yet cold
Soft yet wet
White beauty laying itself
For all to see.
I step outside
Inhale the frosty air
Then I…
Stick my tongue out,
To catch a bit of magic
In my heart.

Winter Friendship Diary #6

And now,
A New Year
To cherish.
A gift of time
To wonder, wander, wish.
To say "I love you"
To listen
To give a hug
To be in the moment
To create memories
To be You
For 31,536,000 seconds.

Winter Friendship Diary #7

The sliver of silver
Sits on the indigo blue sky.
Waiting for…
People to,
See it
Feel it
Rejoice in,
Its curves
Its light
Its magic.
Thank you moon
For another chance
To be present
In the moment.

Winter Friendship Diary #8

To see your white head
Shining in the sun
Atop the electric pole,
My heart skips a beat.
I see you almost every day.
Some days your partner is with you,
Other days you're alone.
I don't have names for you
But I know you're an important
Thread in our community quilt.
Like a true friend by your side
Through it all,
You stand on our bridge pole
A sentry,
Watching over our island,
And probably,
Looking to catch a meal
For your hungry family.
Thank you Bald Eagle
For giving us hope,
Season after season.

Winter Friendship Diary #9

Icicles
Are like desserts.
There to tempt you…
To knock them down
To taste the cool winteriness
To pour maple syrup upon it
To feel like a kid again
Doing something big.

Winter Friendship Diary #10

Dave is one of those friends
Who is on the move, constantly!
Up one branch, down another
Disappearing
Re-appearing
His long toes an anchor.
His bill,
Banging...
Pounding...
Tapping...
Knock knock, anyone home?
His head tilting...
Yes!
Yum!
And more yum!
Up and down the lilac
The sweet pepper bush
And the Hackberry.
His belly full
He stops a moment.
How do you not have a headache, Dave?

Winter Friendship Diary #11

I came around the corner
And my mind did a double take.
Could it be?
This early…
How do they do it?
Pushing through the hard ground
Withstanding the blustery winds
The cold rain and snow.
They survive
To shine their beauty
To give us light
And hope
Of springs coming days.
Thank you Lenten Rose,
For filling my heart
With your cheery gift
On this gray winter day.

Winter Friendship Diary #12

The warmth of a fire
The comfort of a friends laugh
The first daffodils
Can make a cold dark day
Seem filled with light.

Winter Friendship Diary #13

I hear your honking
Low in the sky.
Then the wing flapping,
Then I feel a...
Whooosh .... of air.
I crane my neck
And see the v formation
A black and white moving abstract.
More honking
More flapping
More switching of the guard.
A Chinese fire drill at every cloud.
A new "driver" heading you south.
Rush hour in the sky
Honk, honk, honk...
Safe travels, geese.

Winter Friendship Diary #14

Today,
I met a new friend on the forest trail.
He was there,
Alone
Not moving.
Just lying in the dirt.
I saw him.
I picked him up.
I felt his scratchy bark.
I noticed his stubby ends
And a few scars too.
I named him Arnold.
We are very different.
He's quiet, I'm not.
He comes from a big family, I don't.
He lives outside, I don't (unless I'm camping).
I took him on my walk
And found we like similar things…
We drew in the dirt.
We picked up trash.
We built a fort
And caught snowflakes together.
I took him home.
I introduced him to Mom and Dad
And to Buddy,
Who really liked him,
For who he was.
I'm glad I have a new friend.
Good night Arnold,
I wonder what we'll do tomorrow.

Winter Friendship Diary #15

People talk about gray winter days.
But there are also…
Rust, maroon, olive, blue, tan, white
Chartreuse, black, purple
And orange days.
As friends have different moods,
Days do too.
Sometimes you need to look past
Your initial view,
Listen
Smell
And feel.
What color is your day, today?

Winter Friendship Diary #16

It's cold.
I see my breath
Illuminated by the full moon.
On this peaceful night
I only hear
My footsteps,
Thump, thump, thump
On the pavement.
Creating a soothing rhythm
Like my heartbeat
Or the ocean surf
Or a favorite song.
When out of the blue,
A twig snaps
Something moves…
A white tail
Glowing in the moonlight
Hopping away.
Now I only hear,
Thump, thump, thump
Of my heartbeat racing.
Sorry Jack,
I didn't mean to startle you.
I hope your heart,
Is still thumping.

Winter Friendship Diary #17

Your friendship is for all seasons.
In snow or sun, in wind or rain.
I see you dart and dash
Perch or hang upside down
And hear you sing.
But, I love your call
Chickadee dee dee… Chickadee dee dee…
Always busy this feathered friend.
Can we chat?
I pssh, you look.
I pssh, you fly closer.
I pssh, you call above my head.
Making a fuss. Such a fuss!
So curious. So noisy. So you!
Head cocked this way and that way.
I pssh more, you chatter more.
Soon friends come
Pssh, chatter, pssh, chatter…
Fuss, fuss, fuss!
I stop. You wait.
I watch. You watch.
You fly. I stand.
Bye Charlie
See you soon.

SPRING

Spring Friendship Diary #1

These snow-covered woods
So peaceful
And quiet now…
Hold mysteries
And maps
Of what's been.
Tracks leading here
Circling around
Disappearing under rocks
Into holes.
Popping out again
From under brush
Over the snow mounds
Across the path.
Big paws
Tiny feet
Predator marks
Prey blood.
Some friends
Die younger
Than we want.
What will tonight's
Destiny be…
For my forest friends?

Spring Friendship Diary #2

I see you.
You can't hide.
Your green shoot
And purple bud
So bright
Poking up from under
The blanket of snow,
Beneath last year's
Fallen brown leaves.
The color of hope
For another season,
Another year
Of possibilities,
For this life's journey.

Spring Friendship Diary #3

You settle in
Like a warm blanket
Around the earth.
Somehow,
I feel
Protected
Safe
Calm
When I see the veil of mist
Amongst the trees
Down the street
Kissing the earth.
Thank you Fog,
For knowing
What I needed today.

Spring Friendship Diary #4

Sometimes,
Many times,
Animals, plants, even things
Become so every day.
We stop looking,
Really seeing them.
We stop listening,
Really hearing them.
We stop enjoying,
Really appreciating them.
Thank you Mourning Dove
For your black spots
Pinkish red legs
And bluish eye ring.
For your gentle
Rhythmic
And familiar cooing.
Each morning
Peace
Awakens my soul.
May your eyes
Ears
And heart
Never abandon
The wonderment
These gifts give us.
Whether they are the most common
Or the least common.

Spring Friendship Diary #5

My friends and I
Are not much different
Than the rocks on the beach.
Some are shiny, some not.
Some are big, some tiny.
Some are rough around the edges,
Others are polished soft to the touch.
Some fill up a room,
While others are easily overlooked.

Some are round, others oval,
Others a bit square.
There are 100 shades of
Tans, whites, browns and pinks.
There are the specks, dimples, and fine lines
Which give each one personality.
Sometimes you have to look
Past the exterior,
To be a witness to their inner beauty.

Rocks support each other
And are the heart of the earth.
No matter the size or shape or color
See the individual uniqueness,
And celebrate that.
I sit in awe
Amongst your beauty,
And wonder
Why we're attracted to some
And not to others.

Spring Friendship Diary #6

Relationships,
Like the moon
Wax and wane
Depending on the day, week and month.
For better or worse
It happens.
Embrace the cycle.
Relish the little moments of time.
And the spark of magic
That friendship brings.

Spring Friendship Diary #7

You don't overthink it
Or let fear take over.
You leap…
From the branch
Knowing you'll fly
And glide
Like a kite
Through the sky.
A thermal supporting you
As you get,
A birds eye view
Of what's below.
Smelling for food
As you sail along
On the wind,
In that distinguishable
Black v formation,
Pink head shining in the sun.
People often fear you,
Because they don't know you.
But I,
Thank you Victor,
For being you
For being different
For keeping
My neighborhood clean.

Spring Friendship Diary #8

I hear you!
How can I not!
You're as loud as a trumpet
Even though you're as big as a quarter.
Singing your heart out
For all the world to hear...
PEEP... PEEP... PEEEEEP!!!
All night long
Over and over
Peeping...
Just for the girls.
Warm rainy nights and
Vernal pools don't last forever,
So make hay while you can.
Thank you Spring Peepers
For heralding in spring.
It's the concert of the year
Even if it's not really,
For my ears.

Spring Friendship Diary #9

Some people call you…
Weeds
Not necessary
An unwanted vagrant.
I call you…
Beautiful
A bright light
A necessity.
In early spring…
For bees
Butterflies
And me.
Dandelion flowers now…
Wishes later!

Spring Friendship Diary #10

Sap flowing
Maple trees blooming
Redwing blackbirds singing
Laughing gulls laughing.
Snow drops
Iris
And tête-à-têtes
Dancing on
The brown earth.
Squirrels in a tizzy
A chill in the air
But peace,
That spring is here.

Spring Friendship Diary #11

Laughing above me
Laughing next to me
Laughing in me.
The sound of summer
In late spring
Brings me back
To the beach,
Like it was yesterday
Sitting with my Aunt
Celebrating another day together
At our favorite place.
Thank you Laughing Gull,
For that memory
That summer moment
That keeps my heart
Hopeful,
For another summer
Of creating memories
With someone I love.

Spring Friendship Diary #12

Taking a beach walk
In late spring
Is…
Hoping it's time.
Time for that familiar friend
To come back.
Like they never left.
You know those friends
That you don't see often
But when you do
It's like time has stood still.
You pick right up
Where you left off.
The conversation flowing easily
Your heart joyful
For another chance
Of being in their presence.
As I'm daydreaming…
I sense you.
Out of my peripheral vision
I see a splash,
Maybe a tail
Then…
A shiny grayish hump
A fin
Diving…
In and out of the waves.
Then another fin
A smaller one
A calf
Diving…
Right alongside its mom.
When I look out
Into the sun dappled water
I laugh, smile and wave…
Welcome Back Delila and baby
I look forward
To being with you
All summer.

Spring Friendship Diary #13

I wait for you
All spring
Wondering when it will happen.
When you will burst forth
In exuberance
Shouting…
I'm Here!
The light pale pink
The soft white
The dark robust magenta
Petals
Slowly…
Emerging
Stretching
Opening
Reaching for the sun
Dancing in the breeze
Celebrating
Their freedom.
Until…
A wind
Or rain
Shakes them loose
And they become
Soft petal snow,
In the air
In my hair
On the ground.
Thank you
Cherry Blossoms
For that
Magical
Overwhelming
Heart moment.

Spring Friendship Diary #14

It was bright yellow gold
Lying on the damp green moss
Like a spot of sun
On the dark forest floor.
I inched closer
When I realized
It was alive.
Creeping…
Slowly, slowly, slowly,
Over leaves
Under twigs
Inside a rotting log
Leaving behind
A glistening rainbow path.
A map of where it had been.
I knelt down
I peeked in
We came eye to eye.
Then,
I reached out
And touched my new friend.
Squishy, slimy, soft.
It crept further inside
Away from the day.
Have a nice slumber, Sam.

Spring Friendship Diary #15

Like the ocean water
Ebbing and flowing
You arrive in waves
Of 5, 10, 20…
Until thousands have gone by.
Your white streamlined body
Glows against
The baby blue sky.
Your long pointed wings
Flapping
Propelling you forward…
Then,
Turning on edge
The black tip of your wing
Skims the water,
Like a speed skater
Going around a turn.
You're aerodynamics
Amaze me.
Oh how I wish I could fly
Like you my friends.
Safe spring travels
On your journey north, gannets.

Spring Friendship Diary #16

Nature soothes the soul
And lifts the heart.
May you enjoy the little bits
Of beautiful spring magic
Mother Nature is sprinkling
Around the world today.

67

Spring Friendship Diary #17

I lie in the grass
And watch the clouds,
Come and go
With the wind.
Some big and puffy
Like cotton candy.
Others wispy
Like hair.
Some in patterns
That remind me of
Fish scales.
I see a horse
Maybe a turtle
A person's head.

Each time
I look up,
It's different.
A surprise
I didn't expect.
It may look
Like I'm doing nothing,
Wasting my time
Just sitting with
My cloud friends.
But sometimes,
Many times,
It's the "just being" together,
That comforts the soul.

Spring Friendship Diary #18

I found you,
On the side of the path
Curled in a circle
Motionless
Still
Isolated
On a damp, cold gray day.
Hoping
Wishing
Praying…
For sun
For warmth
For life.
The world
Is dreaming
For the same,
My friend.
Here's to…
Brighter days ahead, Ned.

Spring Friendship Diary #19

You know those friends
Who walk into a room
And everyone is drawn to them,
Like a magnet.
You my friend Ollie,
Are like this.
We don't get to see you often
But when we do,
You pull us in…
With your playful manner
Cute whiskered face
And sleek movements
Through the water.
You remind me
To cherish
The few moments
I get to spend
In your company,
Even if it's…
Only once a year.

Spring Friendship Diary #20

You're the kind of friend
I love having around.
So small.
So busy.
And so… talkative!
You flit
You bounce
And hop along
Tail raised like a flag.
Your rusty color
And eye stripe
Barely visible
But for a fleeting moment,
As you search for breakfast
Under the crackly brown leaves.
Then off you fly
Around the corner.
I follow…
Hoping to spy
A spring secret.
I stand quiet and motionless,
As I watch you,
Disappear through the lattice
Under our porch.
I'll be cheering you on,
Mr. and Mrs. Carolina Wren.
And I look forward
To watching your fledglings
Bounce and flit
Around our yard
Chittering away,
Learning the ways of the world.

Spring Friendship Diary #21

I met this new friend
On a blustery
Spring evening
At the compost bin.
The full moon illuminating
His pointy snout
Big eyes
And grayish white fur.
I was a bit shocked
To see him sitting there
Watching me
As I approached
Closer and closer.
I stood, he sat.
I chatted, he listened.
I stared, he stared.
Until finally,
I gave in
And stepped away.
As I peered…
Around the corner,
He was back to his nightly feast
Of eggs shells, fruits and veggie peels.
It was nice to meet you, Pete
Under the sparkling stars
On this spring evening.

Spring Friendship Diary #22

The gray clouds
Cover the sky
Like a blanket.
The light rain
Patters on the deck.
The daffodils and tulips
Bow in the wind
As it whistles
And whips
Through the trees.
Windows open
I feel spring.
I smell spring.
Then I hear it…
The sweet, bubbly song
That arrives every year
As a birthday gift.
My heart flutters.
My eyes pop wide open.
I yell to my husband…
He's back!
Our House Wren is back!
You always sneak in
Under the radar
As a surprise.
Thank you Walter,
For this blessing
For this warmth
On a chilly, damp day.

Spring Friendship Diary #23

A partnership,
That's gone on
For millions of years.
And I'm not even sure
You know each other.
One creature crawls ashore
To lay green eggs
The size of pinheads
In the sand.
The other,
Migrates thousands of miles
And stops to rest and refuel…
On those eggs.
Gathering on the beach
One giving new life,
One taking it away.
There's a flurry of activity
There are raucous sounds
There's the cycle of the natural world
Continuing on.
It's a spectacle.
Thank you Limulus,
For sharing life.

Spring Friendship Diary #24

She dove in
Feeling the soft wet touch against her skin.
Inhaling the salty fragrance
That made her come alive.
The place she always felt was home,
The ocean.
Playing like the sea creatures,
She jumped waves
And dove deep.
She kicked her feet
Propelled her body
And splashed her arms.
She tiptoed across the sandy bottom
And floated on top.
As she swam through the sun-dappled water,
She became one with it.
Her heart was the ocean
And the ocean was her heart.

77

SUMMER

Summer Friendship Diary #1

Herbert and I are friends.
I'm more his than he's mine, I think.
Many days, he's waiting at the edge of the pool.
Often times, in the pool.
And some days, we play hide and seek.
Luckily, I know Herbert's favorite spot.
Don't let him know I told you - under the bushes.
We don't always like to do the same things.
But the one thing we both love - swimming.
Whether it's a pond or pool.
I call it a pool. Herbert says pond.
It's a little of both.
Water, leaves, sun, shade and a few bugs.
Sometimes we play tag, usually I'm it.
Other times we do our own thing.
I like laps, Herbert does not.
Herbert likes diving deep, I don't like breathing under water.
And many times, we are like rafts in the summer sun
Herbert sitting on my foot, as I float along.
Each day we part ways,
Me doing my thing, Herbert doing his.
I hope to see you tomorrow, Herbert.

Today at the pool or pond if you're Herbert,
It was a long game of hide and seek.
At least 30 minutes of "you know who" hiding
And you guessed it, me seeking.
I had just about given up…
When, you'll never guess who, made his appearance.
I figure he was tired of my "seeking skills"
And came to say,
"Here I am, right under your feet!"
He rode on my leg up to the waters edge
And then, in a flash, he was off…
Now we're playing tag.
The games never end with this summer friend.

Surprise!
I just found out Herbert is a twin!
I couldn't believe my eyes!
How did I not know?
Forgive me Herbert 1 & 2
For mixing you up.
Now I need another name.
But who is who?
Will the real Herbert please stand up!
(Wasn't there a tv show like this?)
Oh my, the life of a friend, with twin friends…

Summer Friendship Diary #2

Zoro and I became friends in my yard.
I'm not exactly sure which day we noticed each other,
But that doesn't matter.
He was zooming around,
Gliding this way, darting that way
Above the circle garden.
I was hula hooping, in our grassy patch
Next to the garden.

We're more different than alike.
Zoro can fly, I can't.
But I wish I could.
He has six legs, I have two.
He likes mosquitoes, lots of them, I prefer fruit.
He's iridescent blue and green, I'm various shades of tan.

The one thing we both enjoy - being outside.
Whether it's sitting in a chair or perched on a branch
Moving our hips or flying through the air
Napping in the shade or basking in the sun
We're there, witnessing nature's magic.
Thanks Zoro,
It was a pleasure watching you zip circles around me,
As I did circles with my hoop.
I look forward to meeting again one day.

Summer Friendship Diary #3

Gladys and I met in the flower patch.
I'm not sure we're friends.
I don't think she even noticed me standing there
On the other side of the garden.
I was cutting flowers in the shade, she was sunning herself.

I stood silent, marveling at her bright colors
Sparkling in the morning light,
While she unfurled her tongue
Like a party blower,
To sip her sweet nectar breakfast.
She tastes with her feet, oh how I wish…
Can you imagine asking for an ice cream sample
And then sticking your toes in it!

Gladys flits and flies from flower to flower.
I don't move, not wanting to interrupt the moment.
She lives a whole big life in a few months.
I'll live mine in years, if I'm lucky.
Thanks for sharing a little bit of your time with me, Gladys.
And then, just like that,
With nary a goodbye,
But a quick flutter past my face,
She's gone.
I continue cutting and snipping and tending,
For more friends to come.

Summer Friendship Diary #4

It was late one night
When I spied him across the road.
Would he be my friend?
Should I make my way across
Or watch from a distance?
If I was too eager,
I might scare him off
And he'd bolt in a cloud of spray.
Should I say hello, how are you,
What a lovely night for a walk?
Or pretend I don't really see him.
He's furry and four legged, I'm upright.
He's snuffling for bugs to eat,
I'm watching bugs.
He's nocturnal, I'm diurnal.
Except on nights like these,
When the air is filled with sweet honeysuckle scent
And the moon is shining my way.
I'll give him room to do his thing,
While I do mine.
A quick whispered, "Hello Fred,"
'Til we meet again.

Summer Friendship Diary #5

Every summer,
Since I was 4 maybe 5,
I've gone out to play with the fireflies.
Or lightening bugs as some call them.
We love flashlight tag.
They fly, I sit.
They blink, I blink.
They dash, I laugh.
They dot, I smile.
They zig and zag, I run.
They mesmerize and entrance.
These little sparks of light
Creating the biggest imprint on my heart.
The game goes on
Hours go by…
Legs and arms covered in red welts
I drag myself inside 'til tomorrow.
I don't like August.
But then I get a surprise,
Hello Gene!

Summer Friendship Diary #6

I was literally quite startled into this friendship.
You know the kind you didn't plan on,
But run headfirst into them
And voila,
You're best buds.
I was comfy on my beach blanket
Eyes closed, listening to the surf
While the sun warmed my face
When…
Kapoom!
He ran right into my leg.
Really more like under my leg.
I yelped, jumped and looked
To see something tan,
The size of a half dollar,
With lots of legs crawling
Way too close to my bottom.
In the first few seconds
All I could think was,
Huge spider!
When my brain finally registered, ghost crab!
Still too close to burrowing under my bottom,
I quickly scooped him up
And placed him in a sandy footprint.
I used my beach bag like an umbrella.
No gull lunch happening in front of me.
Louie threw sand around
Making his kind of sandcastle
Scurrying back and forth before retreating,
Yes, under my blanket!
Too close to my bottom, again!
So, off I went to swim,
Leaving Louie to do his thing,
While I do mine.
I just hope,
I don't sit in the wrong spot,
When I'm done playing in the ocean.

Summer Friendship Diary #7

It happened so fast,
This new friend.
I was up at dawn
The sun and birds keeping me company
Coffee waking my senses
When I felt a presence nearby.
Perhaps a neighbor
A lost tourist
A stray cat...
I sat waiting, sipping, wondering.
Who shall appear?
Slowly up the side of the deck
Came two furry ears.
Then her dark eyes met mine.
Her leather-like nose twitching...
Curious. Cautious. Crafty.
Her nimble fingers grasped the railing,
She continued her climb.
I didn't move.
I didn't even say hello.
I just sat.
No play date today,
But a fleeting moment in time
Captured in my memory,
As she made her way to our roof,
Sweet dreams, Rose.

Summer Friendship Diary #8

Earlier in the day,
It hopped across the path
Like a piece of dirt cast aside from a shovel.
I looked but didn't really pay attention.
Who or what?
Where or why?
None of these crossed my mind.
I was too interested in my own stuff.
Later that evening,
Sitting on the deck
Our paths crossed again.
Instead of scurrying away, he stayed.
Did Earl want to be my friend?
Did he need something?
Then it began,
The strumming
The melodic
Peaceful, nighttime song.
Over and over…
My symphony, from my friend
Reaching my heart and I was nine again
And summer was quickly turning to fall.
Then she appeared.
It was for her, the music.
They leave. I sit.

Summer Friendship Diary #9

Your friendship won't last long,
It's just that type.
You fly in, you drink, you fly away.
You flutter, my heart flutters.
You pump your tail, my heart pumps.
You sip the sugar water, my heart smiles.
You perch, I sit.
You scratch, preen and fluff, I watch.
You zip around, I get dizzy.
You buzz my ear, my heart sings.
Do I know you?
Have you been here before?
Or is it the pink shirt I'm wearing?
Thank you Curtis,
Your glistening, iridescent feathers
Brightened my world today,
If only for a few minutes.
May you travel safely south
And just maybe,
I'll see you in spring.

Summer Friendship Diary #10

Timothy is a challenging friend.
He likes to dig.
Dig in the grass
Dig in the flower pots
Dig up the spring bulbs
Dig, dig, dig!
Drives me crazy, this digging.
Then he climbs…
Up trees and onto the deck.
Sometimes lying in the sun
But most times,
Chewing the wood.
Every corner piece of wood!
Chew, chew, chew!
I try to be understanding.
I love to dig, when I'm planting flowers.
I do not dig up the flowers.
I eat on my deck, I don't eat the deck!
Timothy, I think you are a furry two year old.
I wonder what you'll be up to next.

Summer Friendship Diary #11

Originally,
I met this new friend in the neighborhood.
Then he took up residence in our yard.
I have to be in the mood for him.
He chatters non-stop, day and night.
You know the kind.
Sometimes he sounds like himself,
Other times, not!
This mimicking...
Fun at first, maddening now.
High pitch trills, low bass notes.
Squeaks and squawks.
Whoops and hollers.
How am I supposed to know
If Maurus is talking to me
Or doing a fly by comedy routine?
I may have to start doing my own impersonations.
Watch out neighbors!

Summer Friendship Diary #12

I should have paid more attention
But I got lost in my garden to-dos
And didn't notice Seth
'Til he had slithered away.
His beautiful yellow stripe and brown markings
Vanishing under my deck
In less than twenty seconds.
He would be good at track and field.
Zero to 10 in the blink of an eye.
Gone in a blur.
I wish I had been walking slowly
But I was on a mission.
If I were more present in the moment,
Instead of thinking about the future
I could have had more time with him.
To watch him sunbathe
Enjoy a tasty snack
Or just be him.
Next time Seth,
I'll be more present
To your presence.

Summer Friendship Diary #13

Some friends sneak up on you,
Quiet as a mouse.
Like they're walking on their tip-toes,
In ballet shoes.
How do they do that, with 8 legs!
How long have you been standing there?
Were you going to say hello?
I'm not a fan of your cousins
Or aunts or uncles, sorry Frank.
But I love you, stilt walker of the woods.
The way your delicate legs
Meander over leaves and logs.
Your rusty, orange body
Glowing in the dappled light.
You stop,
Wave your front legs and wait.
I wave back.
I whisper, Hello
I pick you up.
You tickle.
You creep, crawl and dance your way
Up and down my arm
Like it's a tightrope.
I put you down
And watch you wander off.
Don't go near the pool, I yell,
Feeling like a mommy long-legs.

Summer Friendship Diary #14

Sometimes I arrive
And see you
Rowing your oar-ish legs atop the water.
Other times…
You hide, I peek.
'Til I lift the twentieth golden color leaf
Then you're,
Diving, rowing, diving…
Your silvery air bubble
Glistening in the water's light.
I follow you with my eyes.
You resurface across the pool
Floating in cobbler pose.
You let the water carry you along
'Til I appear…
Diving, rowing, diving, hiding.
You'd be great on the swim team
Unless you hid!
I return to my laps.
You return to being you.
Thank you Walter,
It's always a pleasure.
Until you bite me!

Summer Friendship Diary #15

You're a quiet friend, rarely heard.
I have 'til dusk
Before you make an appearance.
I watch and wait…
You arrive on time.
You begin…
Flying your circuit
Up and down my street
Catching bugs
Dining on the wing.
Up and down
Back and forth
Swooping…
Figure eights
Dosey doe's
Dancing in mid air.
Hours go by.
I'm in awe,
Thousands of bugs
Gone in an hour!
Thank you Barry.
A few less red itchy welts tonight.
Bon appétit!

Summer Friendship Diary #16

I met a new friend today.
A little black medallion
With accents of reddish-orange.
Maybe, half-dollar in size.
I almost didn't say hi.
It's just a leaf or floating debris.
I did a few more laps.
But my heart said, look closer.
I looked again.
Wait…
Could it be…
So unexpected
So exciting
Such joy!
Hi Sarah,
Welcome to the world!
Welcome to the pond!
Welcome to the pool!

Summer Friendship Diary #17

Yesterday was one of those days
When you see everyone you know...
With unwashed hair
Wearing a wet bathing suit
With a zinc oxide face.
I'm not sure it mattered,
What I looked like to them, only I noticed.
My backyard was having some type of summer friends' reunion.
Gladys was sipping nectar on the mist flowers.
Curtis was busy drinking all the sugar water.
Tim finished off the birdseed and planted more peanuts.
Seth slithered under my feet with that "why would you step on me look."
All the while, Charlie fussed and fussed about Tim's eating habits.
Henrietta was doing her own thing.

So, I headed to the pool.
But...
Herbert (plus 8 friends), Zoro (plus 2) and Walter (plus 20 of his cousins) were playing leap frog and tag, while Sarah was swimming, as fast as her little legs would take her.
No laps today!

So, I tried the beach.
And you guessed it...
Louie was out, in broad daylight mind you, terrorizing shoobies, scooting backwards and sideways, faster than anyone thought a crab should go, waving his big white claws in the air like he was in a duel.
I promptly scooped him up and found his hole.

I went home, hot and a tad annoyed.
A nice outside shower...
I opened my car door.
I heard them.
I hoped for the best.
Maurus and Earl were involved in a singing contest.
A loud boisterous face off like they were on American Idol.
I stepped under the faucet and closed my eyes.
The day didn't turn out like I'd imagined, it was better.
Thank you friends, for all the little joys.

Summer Friendship Diary #18

I don't know your name yet.
I heard you first.
A soft hum
Then a loud buzz
Invisible in the yellow flowers.
I'm a nosy neighbor…
I get closer
I peek in
There you are, a golden wiggly body.
Bzzz…
Onto the zinnias.
Bzzz…
And the sedum.
Bzzz…
And the asters.
So. So. Busy.
Your body covered in a fine yellow dust.
Your baskets full of pollen.
Can you imagine carrying groceries home,
In bags on your legs!
Me either.
Thank you for the honey, Henrietta.
Bee friendly!

Summer Friendship Diary #19

I met you by chance
In the middle of the road.
Not a safe place.
I schussed you to the grass.
You didn't argue.
We sat for a bit.
I walked, you waddled.
I talked, you looked.
You stopped, I stopped.
Lots of cars stopped,
Out of curiosity
To take photos
To watch.
Meandering our way…
We had a parade
You and me.
A friend stops.
He gently lifts you up.
Sometimes,
We all need to be carried.
Be safe, Harold.
And enjoy the marsh.

Summer Friendship Diary #20

I don't see you
But I hear the splash.
I see the ripples
Fanning out then disappearing.
I scan the pond.
No luck.
I venture a guess at who you are.
I hear you again.
More ripples.
No luck.
Sometimes
Just knowing a friend is near,
Is all you need.
Thank you Marvin.
I hope the third time's a charm.

Summer Friendship Diary #21

I lift the Hibiscus pot and there you are,
A miniature armadillo.
Rolled up in a ball
Gray and scaly
Quiet and motionless
Like we were playing ghosts in the graveyard.
Boo, I yell.
Nothing.
Green light, I yell
And off you go…
Scurrying on fourteen little legs,
Under another pot.
I lift, you run.
Under and over and around.
A miniature obstacle course.
I stop, you stop.
I pick you up, you roll up.
I open my hand, you unfurl.
Hi doodle bug.
Or is it pill bug?
Or roly poly?
Or potato bug?
So. Many. Names.
I'll call you Arnie.

Summer Friendship Diary #22

Herbert invited all his friends to the pond,
My pool!
Today!
I was grumpy at how crowded it was.
What and who is in the pool?
Can I do my laps?
Will they want to chat?
Will they make waves?
Could I relax?
What was he thinking, this frog!
Well, he was thinking fun…
He was thinking, pool party!
We had a chorus, practically a whole band.
Games, you guessed it, tag.
Aerial acrobatics, my own cirque du soleil.
And some yummy treats, I did not partake in eating!
Thank you Herbert,
For being my first summer garden friend.

Summer Friendship Diary #23

Herbert was "sleeping in" today.
I did too.
It's the fall slowing down thing that happens.
Those cool morning temperatures,
Me snuggled under a blanket
He, under his soil lump.
I tried luring him out to swim,
But he was having none of it.
I don't blame him,
I was just here 20 hours ago.
I think he's waiting to warm up before plunging in.
Not me, I have to work.
I jump!
And paddle and paddle and paddle…
Swim just swim, I tell myself.
It's refreshing!
It's waking me up!
I'll get warm in a minute…

Summer Friendship Diary #24

You know how it is with friends.
Some days are active.
Some lazy.
Some in between.
Today it was half and half.
3 frogs huddled on one log.
3 frogs swimming
And me floating.
Herbert was under the bushes, watching.
I swam. I floated. I closed my eyes.
Savoring what might be my last day,
In my little oasis
Away from home.
Thank you pool,
You awakened my creativity
You brought me new friends
Here's to next year and new adventures.

Summer Friendship Diary #25

You think your friends
Will always be there.
They won't.
No pool party today.
No Herbert.
No Friends.
Just a few dead leaves,
Some seeds,
And a floating twig.
Laps were boring.
I talked to Myself.
My heart was heavy.
Sad.
Lonely.
Even though I knew why.
Sweet hibernation dreams Herbert
And friends.
I hope to see you in spring.
Love always, your summer pond bff.

I am Who I am - Me at 88

My hair is gray
And my skin wrinkled.
My shoulders stooped
And my eyes crinkled.

My heart laughs
And lips smile.
I do what I do
In my very own style.

I feed the birds
And play with kittens.
I go outside
In my hand knit mittens.

I sing with the wind
And splash in the mud.
Make wishes on seed fluff
And lie in the sun.

I skip down the lane
And pick tiny flowers.
I stare at clouds
And while away the hours.

I chat with neighbors
And bow to the moon.
I wave goodnight
Hope to see you again soon.

Reviewers Praise *The Friendship Diary*

In her utterly fresh and original The Friendship Diary, Paige Cunningham introduces every one of us—naturalist or not—to the creatures with whom she shares her garden, her walks, her swims. Sometimes named, sometimes not, these off and on companions make up the texture and personality of her days. In deceptively simple lines, these crystalline portraits capture her friends in language as lovely as "These little sparks of light/Creating the biggest imprint on my heart." The best part is that all of us lucky enough to read them will begin immediately spotting our own best friends with brand new eyes, and composing our own friendship memos in our enchanted minds.

—Robert Michael Pyle, author of Evolution of the Genus Iris, Chinook and Chanterelle, and The Tidewater Reach

In the simplest language, Paige Cunningham conveys what it is to be caught in the thrall of nature. Eye level to a daddy longlegs or standing, toothbrush in hand, for the clamor of geese in a starswept sky, this poet seizes the moment, and brings us along.

—Julie Zickefoose, writer/artist (Saving Jemima, Baby Birds, The Bluebird Effect, Letters from Eden)

We witness by words Paige Cunningham's love affair with nature. To bloom with spring, flourish in summer swelter, blush in fall leaf showers and find solace among bare winter trees. With poems to be absorbed more than read. A pleasure to behold in head and heart.

—Dr. J. Drew Lanham, author (The Home Place, Sparrow Envy), professor, wildlife biologist, birder

The poems are perfect for nature lovers of all observation levels.

—Maureen Morrison, teacher of English/ESL

Paige Cunningham's poems, like the myriad friends she finds in nature, are gems.

—Scott Weidensaul, author of Living on the Wind

Paige Cunningham loves to be out and about in nature, at any hour, of any day, looking for slimy, furry, scaly, or feathered friends. She currently lives in West Cape May, NJ with her husband, two cats, dolphins, ghost crabs, monarch butterflies and the ocean. She works as a teacher, naturalist and artist. This is her third book.

Made in the USA
Middletown, DE
25 November 2020